ABOUT THE AUTHORS

Steve Barlow was born in Crewe, in the UK, and has worked at various times as a teacher, an actor, a stage manager and a puppeteer in England, and in Botswana, Africa. He met Steve Skidmore at a school in Nottingham and the Two Steves began writing together. Steve Barlow now lives in Somerset and sails a boat named *Which Way*, so called because he usually hasn't a clue where he's going.

Steve Skidmore is shorter and less hairier than Steve Barlow. After passing some exams at school, he went on to Nottingham University where he spent most of his time playing sport and doing a variety of heroic summer jobs, including counting pastry pie lids (honest). He trained as a teacher of Drama, English and Film studies, before teaming up with Steve Barlow to become a full-time author.

Together they have written many books, including:
The Mad Myths series
Find out more at:
www.the2steves.net

ABOUT THE ILLUSTRATOR

Sonia Leong is based in Cambridge, in the UK, and is a superstar manga artist. She won Tokyopop's first UK Rising Stars of Manga competition (2005-06) and her first graphic novel was *Manga Shakespeare: Romeo and Juliet*. She's a member of Sweatdrop Studios and has too many awards to fit in this teeny space.

Find Sonia at her website: w

I HERO

Space
Rescue

Steve Barlow and Steve Skidmore
Illustrated by Sonia Leong

EDGE
FRANKLIN WATTS

LONDON·SYDNEY

First published in 2009
by Franklin Watts

Text © Steve Barlow and Steve Skidmore 2009
Illustrations © Sonia Leong 2009
Cover design by Jonathan Hair

Franklin Watts
338 Euston Road
London NW1 3BH

Franklin Watts Australia
Level 17/207 Kent Street
Sydney, NSW 2000

A CIP catalogue record for this book
is available from the British Library.

ISBN: 978 0 7496 9035 9

1 3 5 7 9 10 8 6 4 2

Printed in Great Britain

Franklin Watts is a division of Hachette Children's Books,
an Hachette UK company.
www.hachette.co.uk

Decide your own destiny...

This book is not like others you may have read. *You* are the hero of this adventure. It is up to you to make decisions that will affect how the adventure unfolds.

Each section of this book is numbered. At the end of most sections, you will have to make a choice. The choice you make will take you to a different section of the book.

Some of your choices will help you to complete the adventure successfully. But choose carefully, some of your decisions could be fatal!

If you fail, then start the adventure again and learn from your mistake.

If you choose correctly you will succeed in your adventure.

Don't be a zero, be a hero!

You are the top astronaut at UNSA (United Nations Space Agency). You have flown into space many times. You have also spent several months test-flying new spaceships.

You are the one that UNSA calls if there is an emergency. In the past you've repaired damaged satellites, rescued astronauts from space and even dealt with Alien Life Forms (ALFs).

Early one morning, you are woken by the buzz of your Satvid phone.

"Answer," you say. The video screen flicks on to reveal a worried-looking man.

"We have a Red Alert," he says. "We need you at UNSA HQ immediately. An Agency car is on its way."

"Okay," you reply. "I'll get my things."

You quickly pack your bag and head outside. A sleek, black car is already waiting. You step inside it and the door shuts behind you.

"Good morning. Enjoy the ride," says the car's computer.

As the computer-driven car pulls away, you wonder what danger this new mission will bring.

Now turn to section 1.

1

The car glides to a halt outside UNSA HQ and you head straight to the director's office.

The director of UNSA is waiting for you. "We have a problem," he says.

"And that's why you've called me," you reply. "What is it this time?"

"We have a situation with the UNSA base on the moon," says the director. "Two days ago, we lost all contact with it. We need you to go and investigate. If there is a problem, then you will have to deal with it."

"How will I get there?" you ask.

"You'll fly on your own in the single-seater Dart spaceship," the director says. "It'll be quicker than a shuttle. Speed is important."

You nod. "So I'll be on my own – no back-up crew?"

"That's why we want you for this mission – you're the best. Anyway, it will probably be just routine."

"Or it could be dangerous," you say.

"Will you go?" asks the director.

If you say yes, turn to 46.

If you say no, turn to 8.

2

You hit the fire control switch and the flames die out.

You grip the spaceship's controls tightly and fly through the raging storm. The juddering stops and you realise that you have passed out of the Earth's atmosphere and are in space. You ask the computer to check the instruments.

The computer voice answers. "No major damage."

You make contact with the UNSA mission control. "Everything is okay," you say. "The mission continues…"

Go to 19.

3

You rush into the chamber and hide near the doorway. The alien follows you into the chamber. Before the alien can react, you dash out from your hiding place, and out of the chamber.

The doors shut and you press 'Lock'.

The alien is trapped! It slams against the door, but cannot get out.

You smile. You will contact UNSA back on Earth and they will be able to send a team to deal with the creature.

Go to 50.

4

You step into the hangar. Switching on your helmet light, you see a movement next to an oxygen tank.

If you selected the laser blaster at the beginning of the mission, go to 23.

If you chose the ALF detector, go to 48.

5

You tell the professor you have to go, and make your way to the launch site. You head straight to the control room.

The launch controller looks worried. "We have reports of electrical storms heading our way," he tells you. "It could be dangerous to launch. I think we should wait for twenty-four hours until the storms have passed. But it is your decision."

If you wish to go ahead with the mission, go to 41.

If you decide to delay the launch, go to 18.

6

Before you can move, the door opens. You cry out as an alien creature leaps out and grabs hold of you. You feel your mind slipping away as the creature takes over your body. You have been turned into an alien!

You have failed. If you wish to begin your mission again, go to 1.

7

You switch off your oxygen supply and remove your space suit helmet. A big mistake! The atmosphere in the moon base is unstable – you forgot to check!

You are unable to breathe and you drop to the floor, scramble for your helmet and try to turn your oxygen supply back on. It is hopeless. You clutch at your throat as blackness overtakes you.

Your basic error has cost you your life. Go back to 1.

8

The director frowns. "What sort of hero are you?"

"I'm only joking!" you reply. "Of course I'll go."

Go to 46

9

"What happened?" you ask.

Commander Peters steps forward. "It is all part of an alien invasion plan," she says. "An alien from the Rigus galaxy was sent to take over the moon base. Once it had done this, more aliens would be sent to prepare an attack on Earth."

You look puzzled.

If you wish to ask the commander how she knows this, go to 29.

If you wish to switch on the ALF detector, go to 47.

10

"I'm aborting the mission!" you scream into your radio.

As you press the abort switch, the Dart spaceship takes a direct hit. You wrestle with the controls. It is hopeless. You hear a loud explosion and then nothing…

You have paid the ultimate price. If you wish to begin your mission again, go back to 1.

11

You switch on the communications link. A screen flickers into life and the image of a woman appears.

She begins to speak. "This is Commander Peters, commander of the moon base. We are under attack. An alien life form has been detected. It has been blocking all communications with Earth. It is taking over our —"

The screen goes blank. You realise that this is a critical situation.

If you wish to go to the moon base, go to 43.
If you wish to explore the hangar, go to 4.

12

The meteors keep coming, but you somehow manage to avoid them.

Then as suddenly as it appeared, the meteor storm disappears. You breathe a sigh of relief and report your escape back to mission control.

"Well done," says the director. "Now get some sleep." You turn the spaceship's controls to auto pilot, take a sleeping pill and settle down.

Hours later you wake. The ship is about to enter the moon's orbit. You decide to fly the ship in manually to land as close to the moon base as you can. You have to decide how steep your angle of descent will be.

If you decide to land the ship at 45 degrees, go to 25.

If you decide to land at 75 degrees, go to 40.

13

Taking your equipment, you make your way to the communications room. You stand outside the door and take a deep breath.

If you selected the laser blaster at the beginning of the mission, go to 45.

If you chose the ALF detector, go to 39.

14

You point at the ALF detector. "I'll take this."

"Good choice," says the professor. "It works by reading the DNA structure of any life form. Now do you want me to go over the Dart spaceship controls?"

"I know all about that spaceship," you reply. "I flew it in all the tests when it was first designed."

The professor shakes his head. "But there have been some changes."

If you want to listen to the professor, go to 37.

If you want to get on with the mission, go to 5.

15

As you make your way across the moon's surface to the base entrance, you see a space shuttle standing outside a hangar. You glimpse a strange figure heading towards it.

If you wish to investigate further and go to the shuttle, go to 33.

If you wish to enter the moon base, go to 45.

16

You pull back on the controls and hit the reverse rocket boosters. But it is too late. Your ship hurtles towards the surface of the moon.

There is a thunderous noise and your ship is ripped apart. You look back helplessly towards the Earth. It is the last sight you see before you plunge into oblivion.

If you wish to begin the adventure again, go back to 1.

17

As you pull the trigger, the alien dodges. The stream of energy from the weapon misses the creature and hits an oxygen tank. Too late, you realise that you have made a fatal mistake. There is a huge explosion and a deadly fireball engulfs you.

Your lack of thought has cost you your life. If you wish to begin again, go to 1.

18

"It's too dangerous," you say. "We should delay."

The launch controller nods. "I'll tell the director."

Ten minutes later your Satvid phone rings. It is the director. He is furious. "You coward!" he says. "This mission was urgent! I'll get another astronaut to go – one who isn't scared of bad weather. You'll never work for us again. Get off my base!"

Before you can say anything, the director rings off. By not putting the mission ahead of your safety, you have failed. It is the end of your career.

If you want to be a hero, you can start the mission again by going back to 1.

19

Hours pass. Soon, the Earth is far behind and you look out of the window into the blackness of space.

Suddenly an alarm goes off. The computer's loud voice fills the cabin: "WARNING! WARNING! Unidentified objects ahead!"

You look at the computer's radar. There are dozens of white dots on the screen. You are heading straight into a meteor storm! What should you do?

If you want to abort the mission, go to 10.

If you want to switch on the computer's auto flight, go to 44.

If you want to fly the spaceship yourself, go to 49.

20

You stare out of the window. The moon base is about two hundred metres away.

You switch on your com link to Earth. A message appears on the screen:

ALL EARTH–MOON COMMUNICATION SIGNALS BLOCKED

You wonder what could be causing this and then realise that your emergency communication radio is useless. You are on your own. You are wearing your life support systems and body armour. You pick up the rest of your equipment.

"Open the door," you tell the onboard computer.

The metal doors open and you step onto the surface of the moon.

If you wish to head straight to the moon base entrance, go to 15.

If you wish to look around the outside of the base, go to 28.

21

Using your sat nav device, you carefully make your way along the metal corridors of the moon base. There is no sign of life. Eventually you reach the door to the life support systems area. You get ready to enter.

If you selected the laser blaster at the beginning of the mission, go to 45.

If you chose the ALF detector, go to 34.

22

You point at the laser blaster. "I'll take this."

"Good choice," says the professor. "Do you want me to go over the Dart spaceship controls?" he asks.

"I know all about that spaceship," you reply. "I flew it in all the tests when it was first designed."

The professor shakes his head. "But there have been some changes."

If you want to listen to the professor, go to 37.

If you want to get on with the mission, go to 5.

23

You prime your weapon and slowly move forward.

Peering into the darkness, you see the outline of a figure. You gasp: it is not human – it is like nothing you have ever seen before.

If you wish to shoot the creature, go to 17.

If you wish to signal it to come towards you, go to 38.

23

24

You open the door and step inside. The room is full of computer screens, showing the status of the moon base. There are lots of flashing red lights. You realise that you can control all life support systems from here.

You sit at the control desk and order the computers to repair and stabilise the atmosphere in the moon base so that you can breathe without your helmet on.

Minutes later, the computers give the all-clear and you take off your helmet. You wonder where the ALF might be and if there are any crew left alive.

If you wish to check the computer for any clues, go to 36.

If you wish to head back into the base straight away and search for the crew, go to 45.

25

Your angle of descent is good.

The spaceship slows down and the surface of the moon gets nearer. You can see the base ahead. You switch on landing controls and fly in. Descent rockets slow the ship down.

You are a great astronaut. The moon dust is hardly disturbed as you make a perfect landing.

Now go to 20.

26

You hurry after the alien, but by the time you reach the hangar doorway, it has disappeared from sight. You decide to head to the moon base.

Go to 43.

27

You pull the trigger. Your aim is true and the figure drops to the floor. You rush forward and cry out in despair. You have shot one of the crew! She must have been hiding. As you kneel over the dead crew member, you hear a noise behind you. You spin round and scream in terror as an alien creature grabs hold of your head. You feel your mind slipping away as the creature takes over your body. You have been turned into an alien!

You have failed. If you wish to begin your mission again, go to 1.

28

To the left of the moon base, you see a space shuttle standing outside a hangar.

If you wish to investigate the hangar, go to 4.
If you wish to investigate the shuttle, go to 33.

29

"How do you know this?" you ask.

Commander Peters smiles. "Because I am the alien!" In an instant, the commander transforms into an alien creature.

It grabs hold of your head. You struggle, but cannot break free of its deadly grip. You feel your mind slipping away as the creature takes over your body. You have been turned into an alien!

You have failed. If you wish to begin your mission again, go to 1.

30

You make your way to the briefing room. Professor Stevens is waiting for you.

He hands out the special equipment you will take. This includes life support systems, body armour, an energy pistol, special sat nav maps of the base and an emergency communication radio.

Then he points at two items. One is a huge gun and the other is a large backpack with a hand-held scanner. "A laser blaster and an alien life form detector," explains the professor.

You look at the size of the items and shake your head. "I won't be able to carry it all," you say. "I'll have to move quickly. I'll only take one of these."

If you want to take the laser gun go to 22.
If you want to take the ALF detector go to 14.

31

"Come out," you shout.

You gasp as a woman steps out of the shadows. "I'm Commander Peters," she says. "I thought you might be the alien, that's why I was hiding. We were attacked. I'm the only one left alive. It was terrible…"

If you wish to hear the commander's story, go to 9.

If you wish to switch on the ALF detector, go to 47.

32

You check the atmosphere in the moon base. There is little oxygen – you are glad you didn't remove your helmet.

You take out your com link device and bring up the sat nav map of the base. As you move through the corridors, there is no sign of any living thing – alien or human. Turning a corner, you come to a dead end with two doors.

If you wish to enter the control room, go to 24.

If you wish to enter the communications room, go to 45.

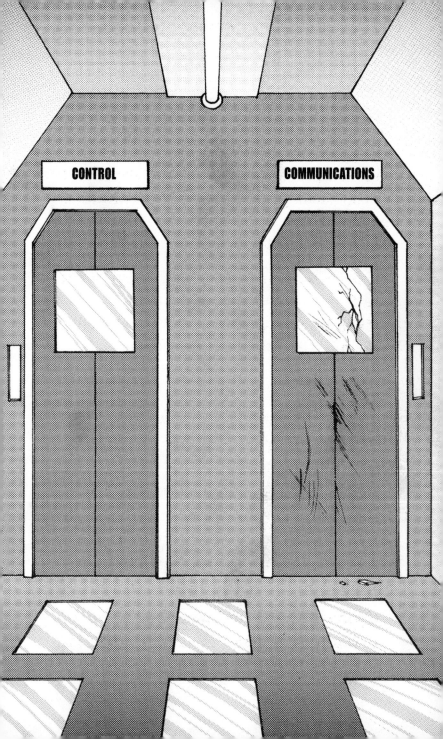

33

You make your way to the shuttle. A ladder leads up to an open door on the space craft. You climb up into the shuttle and head towards the cockpit. There is a light flashing on the communications panel. At that moment you glance out of the window and see something moving in the hangar.

If you wish to listen to the message on the communications panel, go to 11.

If you wish to explore the hangar, go to 4.

34

You press the button for the door. It opens and you step inside.

As the lights flicker on you see a figure moving in the shadows near the oxygen tanks. You reach for your energy pistol.

If you wish to shoot at the figure, go to 27.

If you wish to order the figure to come out, go to 31.

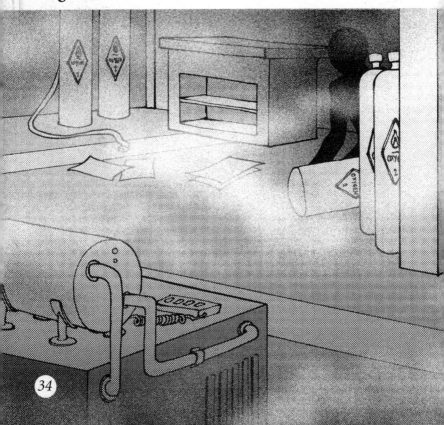

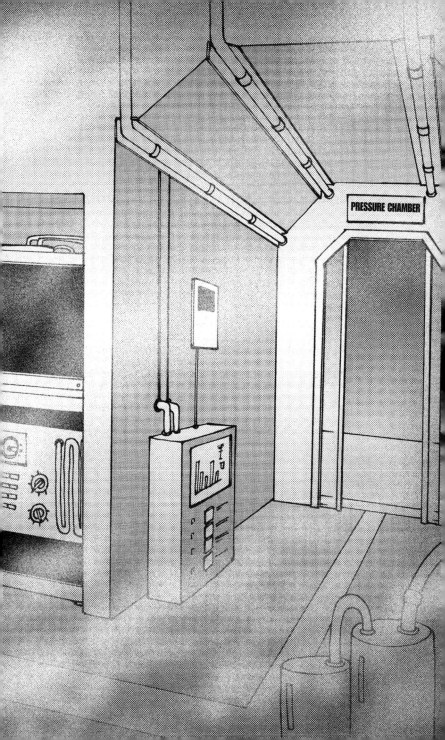

PRESSURE CHAMBER

35

5...4...3...2...1... BLAST OFF!

You are thrust back into your seat by the g-force as the spaceship hurtles upwards.

Suddenly the Dart judders uncontrollably and everything goes black inside. You realise that a lightning bolt has hit the spaceship. Emergency lights snap on. Flames flicker from the control panel. You have to make a quick decision.

If you wish to abort the mission, go to 10.

If you think you can deal with the situation, go to 2.

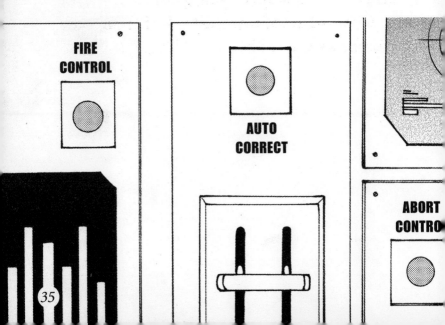

36

You try to access the logs, but all records and entries have been deleted.

You order the computer to scan the moon base for any signs of life.

Within seconds there are two positive readings. The computer speaks: "There are signs of life in the communications room and the life support systems area."

"Alien or human, and how many?" you ask.

"Unable to process," replies the computer. You wonder where you should begin your search.

If you wish to investigate the signs of life in the communications room, go to 13.

If you wish to investigate the life support systems area, go to 21.

37

"What do I need to know?" you ask.

"There's a problem with the computer's auto flight control," says the professor. "You can't rely on it, especially if you were trying to fly through a meteor storm. If that does happen, then switch to manual."

"Thanks, I'll remember that."

"And another thing," says the professor. "When you want to land, set the computer's landing entry to 45 degrees."

Now go to 5.

38

You point the weapon at the alien creature and signal it to move. Suddenly, it leaps forward and heads towards the hangar door at incredible speed.

If you wish to shoot the alien, go to 17.
If you want to follow it, go to 26.

39

You switch on the ALF detector and point it towards the door. The screen flashes red – there is an alien life form in the communications room!

If you wish to enter the communications room, go to 45.

If you would prefer to search for the crew, go to 6.

40

Your angle of descent is too steep! The ship shakes uncontrollably and speeds up. The surface of the moon is getting nearer.

If you wish to change your angle of descent to 45 degrees, go to 25.

If you wish to continue on this angle, go to 16.

41

"This mission is too important to delay," you say. "I'll take the risk."

You make your way to the pre-launch room and put on your space suit. Your chosen equipment is taken on board the Dart.

You head out on to the launch pad where your Dart spaceship is waiting. You notice dark clouds and lightning bolts flashing in the distance. This could be a dangerous take-off, you think.

You climb in and settle into your seat. The spaceship's door is shut behind you.

You make the final checks and get ready for the launch.

The countdown begins: 10…9…8…7…6…

Go to 35.

42

At the far side of the room, you see a pressure chamber. You know that this is used for treating astronauts who have suffered de-compression accidents. You run towards it. The alien chases after you. You reach the chamber and quickly open the door.

If you wish to enter the pressure chamber, got to 3.

If you wish to shoot the alien, go to 17.

43

You arrive at the moon base entrance and open the airlock door. You step inside and close the outside lock. There is a hiss of air. You open the inner door.

You move slowly into the base. Moving down a metal corridor, you see that some of the utility pipes have been damaged. Steam pours out, causing your helmet to fog up and making it difficult to see properly.

If you wish to take off your space helmet, go to 7.

If you wish to keep your helmet on and search around, go to 32.

44

You switch on the auto flight as the meteors hurtle towards you. The ship is buffeted by the deadly storm.

A meteor hits the ship. The auto pilot isn't working! Another meteor hammers into the metal creating a huge hole.

The cabin is filled with wailing alarms and flashing lights. You try to switch off the auto pilot. It is too late! Another meteor hits.

The last thing you see is a flash of light as your spaceship is smashed apart.

If you want to begin the mission again, go back to 1.

45

You press the door button. As it opens, you gasp in horror. Standing before you is an alien creature! Before you can reach for your weapon, it grabs hold of you. You feel your mind slipping away as the creature takes over your body. You have been turned into an alien!

You have failed. If you wish to begin your mission again, go to 1.

46

The director smiles. "I knew you wouldn't let me down. Read this," he says, handing you a briefing document.

You quickly flick through the e-book and take in the important points.

There are 12 men and women living on the moon base. Nothing has been heard from them, not even a distress signal. Recent images from satellites in Earth's orbit show no sign of an explosion or any damage to the base.

"You leave in six hours," says the director. "That will give you time to prepare for the mission. Good luck."

Now go to 30.

47

You quickly switch on the ALF detector. The screen immediately turns red.

"So you know what I am!"

You look up and see the commander transforming into an alien creature.

If you want to shoot the creature, go to 17.
If you wish to try to escape, go to 42.

48

You switch on your ALF detector and point it towards the oxygen tanks. The LCD screen flashes red – there is an alien life form hiding behind them! Slowly, you reach for your energy pistol.

If you wish to retreat to the moon base, go to 43.

If you wish to head towards the ALF, go to 23.

49

You switch the ship to manual flight.

You grip the controls tightly. The first meteor heads towards you and you flick the ship away from the deadly object.

Another meteor hurtles towards you. Again you steer the ship away. Your heart races as you guide the ship through the storm. Time after time, you are nearly hit, but you just manage to avoid the deadly meteors.

However, as the minutes pass, you realise that you are getting tired.

If you wish to abort the mission, go to 10.
If you wish to carry on, go to 12.

50

You head back to the communications room and place the ALF detector against the door.

There are no signs of alien life, so you open the door. Inside are the crew of the moon base. They thank you for rescuing them. You order some of the crew to guard the pressure chamber.

Back in the control room, they tell you the story of how the alien took over Commander Peters and imprisoned them all.

Now that the alien is captured, the communications link to Earth is restored. You contact the director and inform him of your adventure.

"Well done," he says. "The Earth is safe for now! The alien cannot contact its home planet. The plan to invade Earth has failed! You are a real hero!"

All these I, Hero titles are available now!

Strike Force
Steve Barlow – Steve Skidmore

978 0 7496 9036 6

Pirate Gold
Steve Barlow – Steve Skidmore

978 0 7496 8264 4

Save the Empire!
Steve Barlow – Steve Skidmore

978 0 7496 8265 1

Code Mission
Steve Barlow – Steve Skidmore

978 0 7496 7667 4

Death or Glory!
Steve Barlow – Steve Skidmore

978 0 7496 7664 3

Gorgon's Cave
Steve Barlow – Steve Skidmore

978 0 7496 7666 7

Viking Blood
Steve Barlow – Steve Skidmore

978 0 7496 7665 0

Strike Force

Steve Barlow and Steve Skidmore

Illustrated by Sonia Leong

You are a member of Strike Force, a Special Forces operations squad. You have taken part in many dangerous missions throughout the world. Strike Force agents are only called in as a last resort and you are on standby 24 hours, 7 days-a-week.

As a senior member of the force, you are a martial arts and weapons expert. You also speak many languages. One morning you are training in the Strike Force base gym, when a soldier enters and salutes. "Nemesis wishes to see you straight away. It's a Code Black," he says. Nemesis is the codename for your boss, and Code Black is the highest mission level. Whatever task lies ahead for you, it is going to be very dangerous.

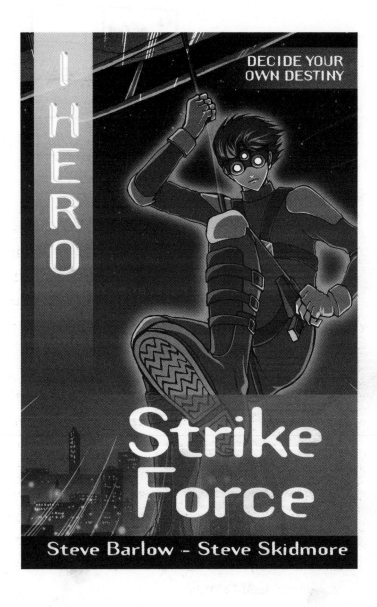

I HERO

Strike
Force

Steve Barlow – Steve Skidmore

Ls 06/09	Lm 3|12